The Perfect Spot

by **Alice Hemming**

illustrated by
Gisela Bohorquez

I cannot see a thing to paint.

4

I will find the perfect spot to paint.

Off I go!

This is perfect. I can see the river.

But...

...the bins! What a pong!

Off I go!

Puff, puff! This hill is big!

13

But I can see a tree on top of the hill.

This is a perfect spot.

But...

...the birds! What a fuss!

Cheep, cheep!

Off I go!

19

This is much better.

I can see the sheep.

But...

...*what* is that racket?

How sad. I will never find the perfect spot.

Or will I? Off I go!

Now I have the perfect spot...

...back in the shed!

28

Quiz

1. Where do I go first?
a) To the river
b) To see the birds
c) To the hill

2. Why is the river not the perfect spot?
a) Because it is sad
b) Because it is too smelly
c) Because it is a fuss

3. Puff, puff! This hill is _____!
a) Better
b) Perfect
c) Big

4. What animals do I see?
a) Cats and dogs
b) Sheep and birds
c) Pigs

5. Where is the perfect spot in the end?
a) The shed
b) The hill
c) The river

Turn over for answers

Book Bands for Guided Reading

The Institute of Education book banding system is a scale of colours that reflects the various levels of reading difficulty. The bands are assigned by taking into account the content, the language style, the layout and phonics. Word, phrase and sentence level work is also taken into consideration.

Maverick Early Readers are a bright, attractive range of books covering the pink to white bands. All of these books have been book banded for guided reading to the industry standard and edited by a leading educational consultant.

To view the whole Maverick Readers scheme, visit our website at
www.maverickearlyreaders.com

Or scan the QR code above to view our scheme instantly!

Quiz Answers: 1a, 2b, 3c, 4b, 5a